Big Pig on a dig

Russell Punter
Adapted from a story by Phil Roxbee Cox
Illustrated by Stephen Cartwright

Designed by Helen Cooke
Edited by Jenny Tyler and Lesley Sims
Reading consultants: Alison Kelly and Anne Washtell

There is a little yellow duck to find on every page.

A letter lands on
Big Pig's mat...

For buried treasure, find this hat!

Big Pig

So Big Pig hunts.
She finds the hat...

...and, tucked inside, a dusty map!

"Fat Cat!" she shouts.
"Look what I've found."

She lays the map down on the ground.

A big cross shows where she should dig.

"A chest of treasure!" cries Big Pig.

Off you trot, and let me rest.

Big Pig heads off to find the chest.

Fat Cat grins. "That funny pig."

"I'll go along to watch her dig."

But first, Fat Cat decides to nap...
and dreams of cream.

Yum!

Lap, lap, lap!

"There's the cross!" declares Big Pig.

"This will be fun. I love to dig."

She's so excited by the dig...

...she does a jig upon a twig!

With hat and shovel, she's all set.

"There's loads of gold to find, I'll bet."

"I'll soon be rich!"
Big Pig digs down...

...deeper, deeper.

Not long now!

Big Pig hurls dirt
beyond the hole.

Now she's closer to her goal.

But who's this digging by her side?

"Have you found gold there?"
Big Pig cries.

"Who put this old box in my hole?"

"Chocolate coins! Why, thanks Fat Cat. How kind of you to do all that!"

Puzzles

Puzzle 1
Find these things on Big Pig's map.

bridge
ducks
pond
river
ship
treasure chest
trees

Puzzle 2
Which word is wrong
on Big Pig's letter?

For buried treasure, find this cat!

Big Pig

Puzzle 3
Spot the six differences between these pictures.

Puzzle 4
Which five things are <u>not</u> in the picture?

bee	map
butterfly	mat
flowers	shovel
helmet	snail
letter	tree

Answers to puzzles

Puzzle 1

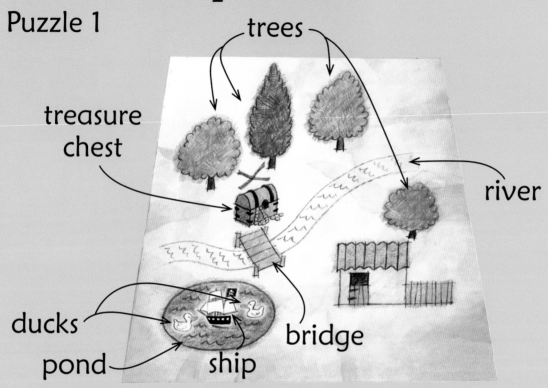

trees

treasure chest

river

ducks

pond

ship

bridge

Puzzle 2

Big Pig

For buried treasure, find this <u>hat!</u>

Puzzle 3

Puzzle 4
These five things are <u>not</u> in the picture:

helmet

letter

mat

shovel

tree

About phonics

Phonics is a method of teaching reading used extensively in today's schools. At its heart is an emphasis on identifying the *sounds* of letters, or combinations of letters, that are then put together to make words. These sounds are known as phonemes.

Starting to read

Learning to read is an important milestone for any child. The process can begin well before children start to learn letters and put them together to read words. The sooner children can discover books and enjoy stories and language, the better they will be prepared for reading themselves, first with the help of an adult and then independently.

You can find out more about phonics on the Usborne Very First Reading website, **usborne.com/veryfirstreading** (US readers go to **veryfirstreading.com**). Click on the **Parents** tab at the top of the page, then scroll down and click on **About synthetic phonics**.

Phonemic awareness

An important early stage in pre-reading and early reading is developing phonemic awareness: that is, listening out for the sounds within words. Rhymes, rhyming stories and alliteration are excellent ways of encouraging phonemic awareness.

In this story, your child will soon identify the *i* sound, as in **pig** and **dig**. Look out, too, for rhymes such as **mat** – **hat** and **mole** – **hole**.

Hearing your child read

If your child is reading a story to you, don't rush to correct mistakes, but be ready to prompt or guide if he or she is struggling. Above all, give plenty of praise and encouragement.